# The Bach Double Violin Concerto Study Book

## Volume One: First Movement

## by Cassia Harvey

### edited by Myanna Harvey

CHP342

www.charveypublications.com

**This book divides the first movement of J. S. Bach's Concerto for Two Violins in D minor into short sections and provides exercises for mastering each section.**

The exercises are written to benefit both the professional and the student.

Each exercise was written to teach a specific skill. **Shifts** are often repeated to help with acquiring muscle memory. **Double stops** are included for establishing relative pitch, building left-hand strength, and balancing the bow across two strings.

Because it only uses the first several position, at first glance, this movement may appear easier than it is. However, Bach's music is deceptively simple, and significant left and right-hand skills are required to play it well. This book attempts to help violinists competently play the Concerto so that they can add their own interpretation.

Before these bowings and fingerings were chosen, several editions were studied. In cases where multiple fingerings or bowings are possible, we chose the most common or most practical options. In these cases, exercises are included for each option. In several cases where including an alternate bowing would be too crowded on the page, exercises for that bowing are included at the end of the movement.

## Notes on Technique

### Bowings

Unless otherwise marked, begin each exercise on a down bow (⊓).

If you change the bowings in a movement, go ahead and change the related bowings in the exercises wherever possible. The bowings in the exercises should be as close to the performance bowings as possible.

### Fingerings

If you change the fingerings for any part of the Concerto, go ahead and change the related fingerings in the exercises wherever possible.

### Tempo

Many of the exercises were written with slower note values than the Concerto so that the piece can be learned at a slower pace. In addition, exercises can be played with increasing speed, eventually reaching the performance tempo.

### Positions

Shifting is indicated by a finger number. Stay in position until a new fingering indicates another shift.

### Strings

Strings are indicated by Roman numerals under the notes.
I=E string, II=A string, III=D string, IV=G string

## Some Interpretation Ideas

**Bowing**: Bowing in the Concerto is typically played *on* the string. Separate bows could be played with connected notes or with the notes slightly separated.

**Shifting**: Shifts can be rapid and clean, without excessive sliding sounds.

**Tempo**: With a tempo marking of *Vivace*, this movement should be played at an appropriately lively tempo, once learned.

## Dynamics

Violinists often choose to use dynamics that follow the phrase or sentence of music. When the notes go up scale-wise, a crescendo can be played. When the notes go down, a decrescendo can be played. However, this is only a starting point. There are a number of cases (for example, measure 22 of the Violin One part or measure 26 of the Violin Two part) where a crescendo could work well as the phrase goes down. As you play, pencil in dynamics that make sense to you and then keep them if they stand the test of repeated playing.

Some notes are more important than others. Once you have learned the natural (or obvious) technique of the Concerto, you can spend a lifetime deciding which notes to elevate above others and thus avoid playing in a monotone. Traditionally, these elevated or favored notes are played after a crescendo to make their importance more believable.

# The Bach Double Violin Concerto Study Book, Volume One
## Table of Contents

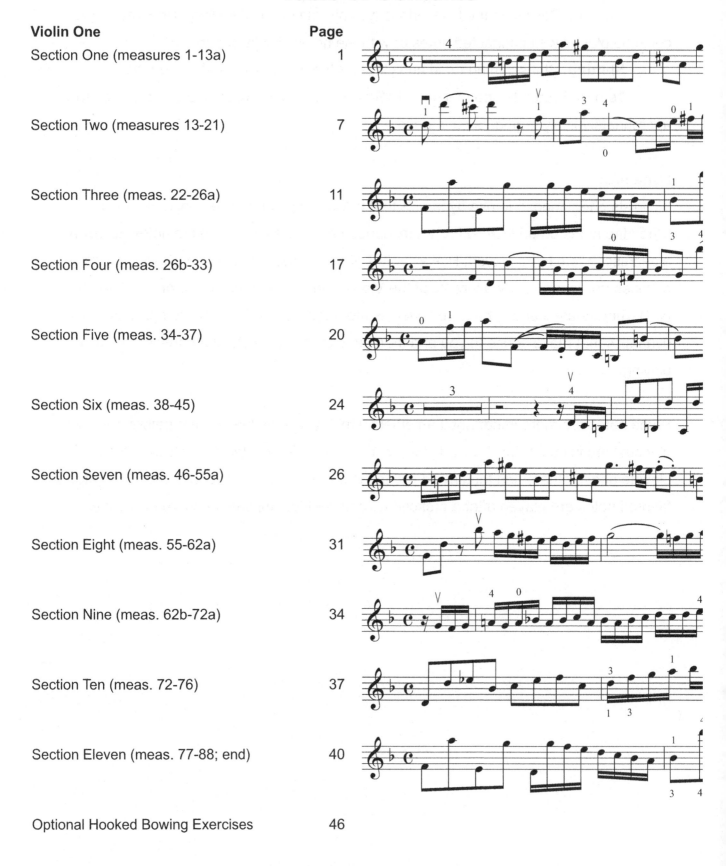

Note: The Concerto is broken up into sections in this study book. The complete first movement is at the back of the book.

Concerto by J. S. Bach
Exercises by Cassia Harvey

# Concerto
## Violin One, Section One: Measures 1-13a

Note: if hooked bowings are used in measures 10-12, they can be studied using the exercises on page 46.

# Intonation
## Measures 5-6

Key of D minor: B♭

# Finger Exercise
## Measures 5-6

# Double Stops for Intonation
## Measures 5-6

## Intonation: Bottom Fingering
### Measure 7

## Finger Exercise: Bottom Fingering
### Measure 7

## Shifting: Top Fingering
### Measure 7

## Learning the Notes: Top Fingering
### Measure 7

## Double Stops for Intonation: Top Fingering
### Measure 7

# Learning the Notes
## Measures 8-9

More exercises for the trill in
measure 8 can be found on page 48.

# Finger and Bow Exercise
## Measures 10-12

Note: The lines under the notes represent bow length. In order to return to the frog after the initial down bow, use more slightly more bow on each up-bow.

# Bow Distribution Exercise I
## Measures 10-12

# Bow Distribution Exercise II
## Measures 10-12

# Bow Distribution Exercise III
## Measures 10-12

# Shifting
## Measure 13

Return to play the excerpt on p.1 before continuing with p.7.

# Concerto
## Violin One, Section Two: Measures 13-21

## Learning the Notes
### Measures 13-17

# Finger Exercise
## Measures 14-17

# Shifting
## Measures 17-18

# Intonation
## Measures 18-19

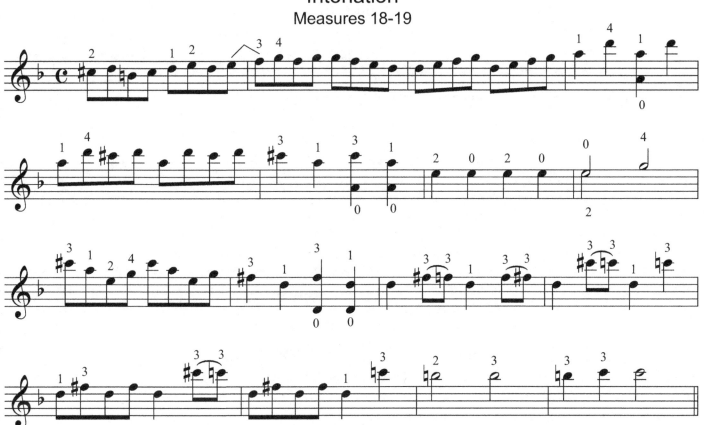

# Shifting Back to Second Position
## Measure 19

# More Second Position
## Measures 19-20

# Second to Third Position
## Measures 20-21

More exercises for the trill in
measure 21 can be found on page 49.

**Return to play the excerpt on p.7 before continuing with p.11.**

# Concerto
## Violin One, Section Three: Measures 22-26a

Note: if hooked bowings are used in measures 25-26, they can be studied using the exercises on page 47.

## Intonation Across Strings
### Measure 22

(vibrato)

(vibrato)

## Shifting and Playing Across Strings I: Top Fingering
### Measures 22-24

## Shifting and Playing Across Strings II: Top Fingering
### Measures 22-24

## Shifting and Playing Across Strings III: Top Fingering
### Measures 22-24

## Shifting and Playing Across Strings I: Bottom Fingering
### Measures 22-23

## Shifting and Playing Across Strings II: Bottom Fingering
### Measures 22-24

## Shifting and Playing Across Strings III: Bottom Fingering
### Measures 22-24

## Shifting Intensive: Top Fingering

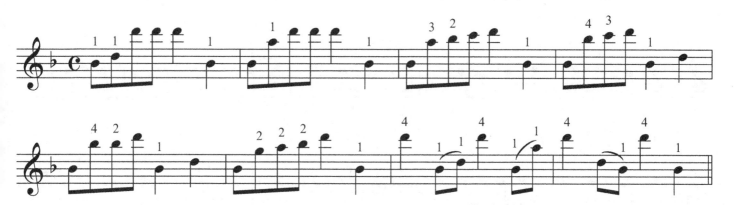

## Shifting Intensive: Bottom Fingering

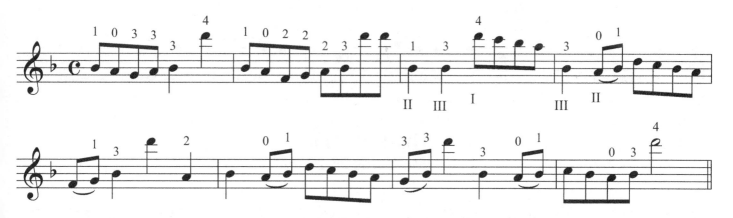

## String Crossing: Top and Bottom Fingerings
### Measure 23-25

# Learning the Notes
## Measure 25

# Third Position
## Measures 25-26

## Shifting and Finger Positions: Measures 25-26

**Return to play the excerpt on p.11 before continuing below.**

# Concerto
## Violin One, Section Four: Measures 26b-33

Note: if hooked bowings are used in measures 25-26,
they can be studied using the exercises on page 47.

## Double Stops for Intonation: Measures 26-27

## Advanced Double Stops: Measures 27-29

## Bowing
### Measures 27-29

## Shifting I
### Measure 29

## Shifting II
### Measure 29-30

## Shifting III
### Measure 29-30

# Intonation
### Measures 29-33

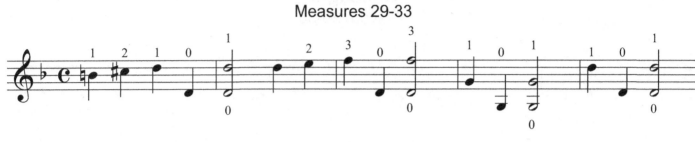

**Return to play the excerpt on p.17 before continuing below.**

# Concerto
## Violin One, Section Five: Measures 34-37

# Intonation and Bowing
## Measures 34-35

# Shifting I
## Measures 35-37

## Shifting II
### Measures 35-37

## Shifting III
### Measures 35-37

## Positions
### Measures 35-37

# Learning the Patterns
## Measures 35-37

# Fluency
## Measures 35-37

**Return to play the excerpt on p.20 before continuing with p.24.**

# Concerto
## Violin One, Section Six: Measures 38-45

### String Crossing I: Measures 41-43

### String Crossing II: Measure 42

### String Crossing III: Measure 43

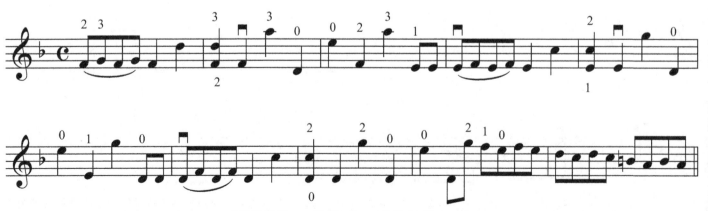

# Learning the Notes: Top Fingering
## Measures 44-45

# Shifting and Finger Patterns: Top Fingering
## Measures 44-45

# Learning the Notes: Bottom Fingering
## Measures 44-45

Shift; don't stretch.

Return to play the excerpt on p.24 before continuing below.

# Concerto
## Violin One, Section Seven: Measures 46-55a

More exercises for the trill in
measure 49 can be found on page 48.

## Review: Measures 46-49

## Intonation: Measures 50-51

## Shifting: Measure 51

## Third Position: Measures 51-53

## Shifting: Top Fingering
### Measures 51-52

# Fluency: Top Fingering
## Measures 51-53

# Shifting: Bottom Fingering
## Measures 51-52

## Fluency: Bottom Fingering
### Measures 51-53

## Shifting Backwards and Fluency
### Measures 53-55

**Return to play the excerpt on p.26 before continuing with p.31.**

# Concerto
## Violin One, Section Eight: Measures 55-62a

Note: if hooked bowings are used in measures 56-57,
they can be studied using the exercises on page 47.

## Intonation: Measures 55-57

## Finger Exercise: Measures 55-57

# Shifting
## Measures 57-58

# Positions: Top Fingering
## Measures 58-60

# Positions: Bottom Fingering
## Measures 58-60

# Backward Shift
## Measure 60

## Intonation: Measures 60-62

Return to play the excerpt on p.31 before continuing below.

## Concerto
### Violin One, Section Nine: Measures 62b-72a

# Learning the Notes
## Measures 62b-64

# Learning the Bowing on Open Strings
## Measures 64-66

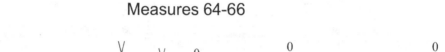

# Learning the Notes
## Measures 67-68

## Hooked Bowing: Measures 69-70

## Bowing: Measures 68-70

## Learning the Notes: Measure 70

## Finger Exercise: Measures 67-69

**Return to play the excerpt on p.34 before continuing with p.37.**

# Concerto
## Violin One, Section Ten: Measures 72-76

## Intonation
### Measure 72

## Shifting: Top Fingering
### Measure 73

## Shifting: Bottom Fingering
### Measures 72-73

## Playing in Third Position
### Measure 73

## Playing in Third Position
### Measures 74-75

## Shifting Back: Top Fingering
### Measure 76

## Shifting Back: Top Fingering
### Measure 76

Return to play the excerpt on p.37 before continuing below.

## Concerto
### Violin One, Section Eleven: Measures 77-88 (end)

Note: if hooked bowings are used in measures 80-82,
they can be studied using the exercises on page 47.

## Third Position Review: Top and Bottom Fingerings
### Measure 77-78

The main exercises for these measures can be found on pages 11-18.

## Review: Top Fingering
### Measure 77-78

The main exercises for these measures can be found on pages 11-18.

# Review: Bottom Fingering
## Measures 77-78

# Intonation Review
## Measures 79-82

## String Crossing Review
### Measures 82-84

## Counting Review
### Measures 84-85

## Finger Exercise
### Measures 84-85

# Learning the Notes
## Measures 85-86

# Shifting: Top Fingering
## Measures 86-88

## Shifting: Top Fingering
### Measures 77-88

## Shifting and Trills: Top Fingering
### Measures 84-88

## Shifting and Trills: Bottom Fingering
### Measures 84-88

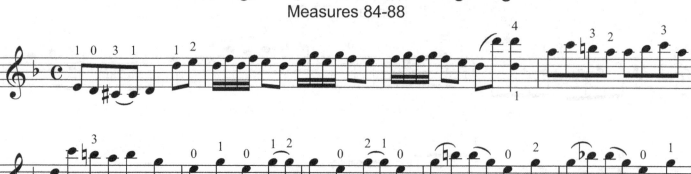

Return to play the excerpt on p.40 before continuing,.

## Optional Hooked Bowing (Not Included in Main Exercises)
### Measures 10-12

## Optional Hooked Bowing (Not Included in Main Exercises): Measures 25-27, 80-82

## Optional Hooked Bowing (Not Included in Main Exercises)
### Measures 56-57

## Trill Study I: Measures 8, 49

## Trill Study II: Measures 8, 49

## Trill Study III: Measures 8, 49

# Third Position Trill Study I
## Measure 21

# Third Position Trill Study II
## Measure 21

# Third Position Trill Study III
## Measure 21

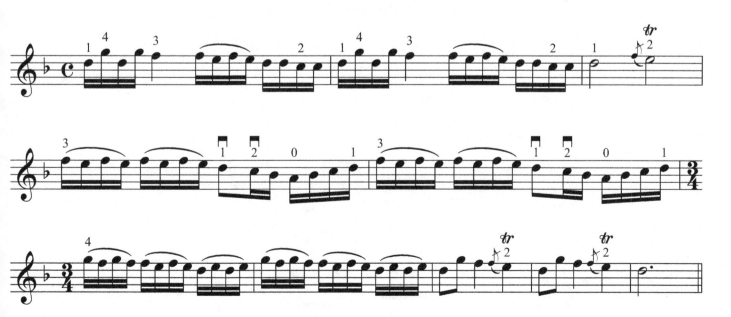

# Concerto
## Violin Two, Section One: Measures 1-13a

Note: if hooked bowings are used in measures 5-6 and 11-12,
they can be studied using the exercises on page 102.

# Intonation
## Measures 1-2

## Finger Exercise
### Measures 1-2

## Double Stops for Intonation: Measures 1-2

## Intonation: Bottom Fingering: Measure 3

## Finger Exercise: Bottom Fingering: Measure 3-4

## Shifting: Top Fingering
### Measure 3

## Learning the Notes: Top Fingering
### Measure 3

## Double Stops for Intonation: Top Fingering: Measure 3

## Learning the Notes: Measures 4-6

## Finger and Bow Exercise: Measures 4-5

More exercises for the trill in m. 4 can be found on pages 101-102.

Note: The lines under the notes represent bow length. In order to return to the frog after the initial down bow, use more slightly more bow on each up-bow.

## Bow Distribution Exercise I
### Measures 5-6

## Bow Distribution Exercise II
### Measures 5-6

## Bow Distribution Exercise III
### Measures 5-6

## Shifting I: Top Fingering
### Measure 7

## Shifting II: Top Fingering
### Measure 7

## Playing in Third Position: Top Fingering
### Measure 7

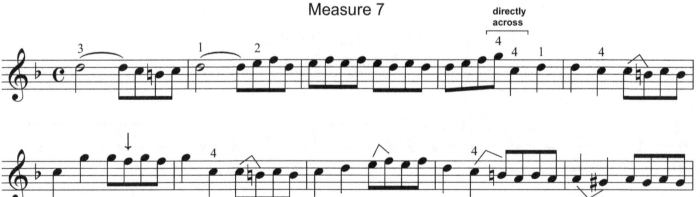

# Rhythm and Shifting: Top Fingering
## Measures 5-9

# Shifting I: Bottom Fingering
## Measure 7

## Shifting II: Bottom Fingering
### Measures 7-8

## Shifting III: Bottom Fingering
### Measures 7-8

## Rhythm and Shifting: Bottom
## Fingering
### Measures 5-9

## Learning the Notes
### Measures 9-13

# Finger Exercise
## Measures 9-13

# Double Stops for Intonation
## Measures 9-13

Return to play the excerpt on p.50 before continuing with p.61.

# Concerto
## Violin Two, Section Two: Measures 13b-21

Note: if a hooked bowing is used in measure 18,
it can be studied using the exercise on page 103.

# Learning the Notes
### Measures 13-14

# Learning the Notes: Top Fingering
### Measures 15-17

## Shifting I: Bottom Fingering
### Measures 15-16

## Shifting II: Bottom Fingering
### Measures 15-17

# Backward Shift: Bottom Fingering
## Measure 17

# Learning the Notes
## Measures 17-20

# Counting
## Measures 17-20

**Return to play the excerpt on p.61 before continuing below.**

# Concerto
## Violin Two, Section Three: Measures 22-33

## Intonation Across Strings: Top Fingering
### Measures 25-27

## Shifting and Playing Across Strings I: Top Fingering
### Measures 26-27

## Shifting and Playing Across Strings II: Top Fingering
### Measures 26-28

## Shifting and Playing Across Strings III: Top Fingering
### Measures 26-28

# Intonation Across Strings: Bottom Fingering
## Measures 25-27

# Shifting and Playing Across Strings I: Bottom Fingering
## Measures 26-27

## Shifting and Playing Across Strings II: Bottom Fingering
### Measures 26-28

## Shifting and Playing Across Strings III: Bottom Fingering
### Measures 26-28

## String Crossing
### Measures 26-29

## Learning the Notes: Top Fingering
### Measures 28-29

# Shifting: Top Fingering
## Measures 29-30

# Shifting and Rhythm: Top Fingering
## Measures 29-31

# Bowing and Rhythm: Top Fingering
## Measures 29-31

# Learning the Notes: Bottom Fingering
## Measures 28-29

## Shifting: Bottom Fingering
### Measures 29-30

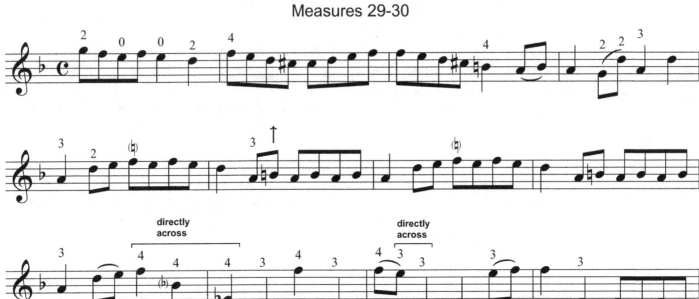

## Shifting and Rhythm: Top Fingering
### Measures 29-31

# Bowing and Rhythm: Bottom Fingering
## Measures 29-31

# Intonation I
## Measures 30-32

## Intonation II: Measures 32-33

Return to play the excerpt on p.64 before continuing below.

## Concerto
### Violin Two, Section Four: Measures 34-45

Note: if hooked bowings are used in measures 41-43,
they can be studied using the exercises on page 103.

## Learning the Notes
### Measures 34-35

## Intonation: Measures 36-37

## String Crossing I: Measures 38-39

## String Crossing II: Measures 38-39

## String Crossing III: Measures 38-39

## Learning the Notes, Top Fingering: Measures 40-41

## Shifting and Finger Patterns, Top Fingering: Measures 40-41

# Learning the Notes: Bottom Fingering
## Measures 40-41

# Learning the Notes
## Measures 42-43

# Shifting I: Top Fingering
## Measures 43-45

# Shifting II: Top Fingering
## Measures 43-45

## Shifting I: Bottom Fingering
### Measures 43-45

## Shifting II: Bottom Fingering
### Measures 43-45

Return to play the excerpt on p.74 before continuing below.

# Concerto
## Violin Two, Section Five: Measures 46-53a

Note: if hooked bowings are used in measures 46-48,
they can be studied using the exercises on page 103.

# Intonation
## Measures 46-47

## Shifting (Top Fingering)
### Measure 48

## Shifting into Second Position (Top Fingering)
### Measure 48

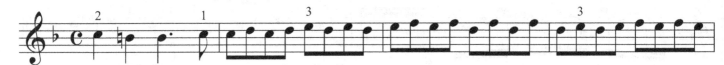

## Playing in Second Position (Top Fingering): Measures 48-49

## Shifting Back from Second Position (Top Fingering)
### Measure 49

## Shifting (Bottom Fingering)
### Measures 48-49

## Intonation: Measures 50-51

## Finger Patterns: Measures 50-51

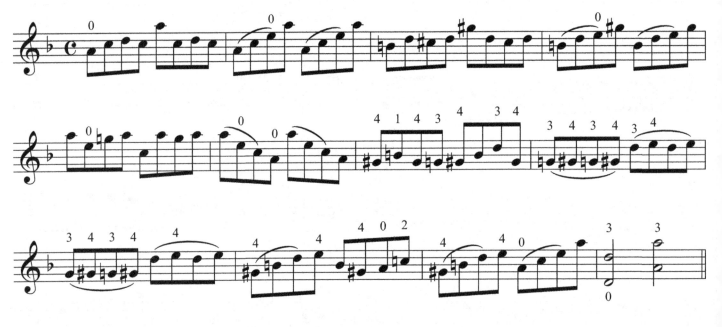

## Arpeggios: Measures 50-51

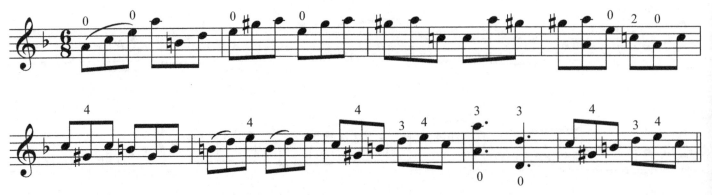

## Shifting: Measure 51

## Shifting and Playing Across Strings I: Measures 51-53

## Shifting and Playing Across Strings II: Measures 51-53

**Return to play the excerpt on p.81 before continuing with p.86.**

# Concerto
## Violin Two, Section Six: Measures 53b-60a

Note: if hooked bowings are used in measures 55-57, they can be studied using the exercises on page 104.

# Intonation
## Measures 53-58

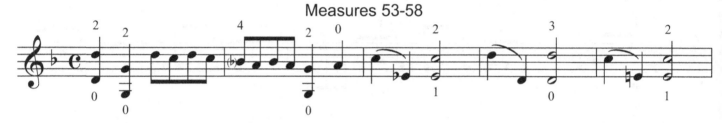

# Finger Patterns
## Measures 54-58

# Shifting
## Measures 58-59

# Playing Across Strings
## Measures 58-60

# Rhythm: Measures 53-58

Return to play the excerpt on p.86 before continuing with p.88.

# Concerto
## Violin Two, Section Seven: Measures 60-68

## Arpeggios I (Top Fingering)
### Measures 60-62

# Arpeggios II (Top Fingering)
## Measures 60-62

# Arpeggios III (Top Fingering)
## Measures 60-62

## Arpeggios I (Bottom Fingering)
### Measures 60-62

## Arpeggios II (Bottom Fingering)
### Measures 60-62

## Arpeggios III (Bottom Fingering)
### Measures 60-62

## Spaces Across Strings in Second Position
### Measures 62-64

## Rhythm and Bowing: Measures 62-64

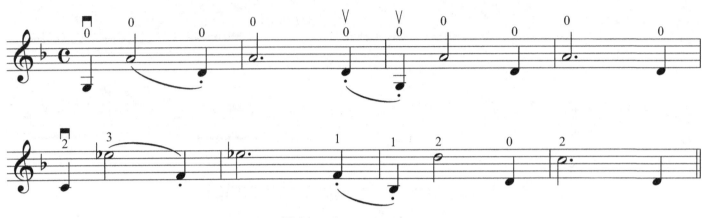

## Finger Exercise: Measures 64-66

## Fluency: Measures 64-66

## Rhythm and Bowing: Measures 66-68

## Concerto

### Violin Two, Section Eight: Measures 69-76

**Return to play the excerpt on p.88 before continuing below.**

## Learning the Notes

### Measure 69

# Shifting
## Measures 69-70

# Intonation
## Measures 70-74

# Learning the Notes
## Measures 70-74

# Shifting (Top Fingering)
## Measures 74-75

# Shifting (Bottom Fingering)
## Measures 74-75

## Bowing and Rhythm (Top Fingering): Measures 73-75

## Bowing and Rhythm (Bottom Fingering): Measures 73-75

## Shifting I
### Measures 75-76

# Shifting II
## Measures 75-76

# Shifting III
## Measures 75-76

# Positions I
## Measures 75-76

## Positions II: Measures 75-76

## Position Challenge: Measures 75-76

## Intonation: Measure 76

## Concerto

Return to play the excerpt on p.93 before continuing below.

### Violin Two, Section Nine: Measures 77-88 (end)

Note: Measures 80-84 are identical to measures 25-29.
Use the exercises on pages 61-67 to work on these measures.

Note: if hooked bowings are used in measures 85-87, they can be studied using the exercises on page 104.

## Learning the Notes (Top Fingering)
### Measures 84-85

# Learning the Notes (Top Fingering)
## Measure 85-86

# Learning the Notes (Bottom Fingering)
## Measures 84-86

# Shifting (Top Fingering)
## Measures 87-88

## Shifting (Bottom Fingering)
### Measures 87-88

## Trill Study I
### Measure 4

## Trill Study II: Measure 4

## Trill Study III: Measure 4

## Optional Hooked Bowing (Not Included in Main Exercises): Measures 5-6. 11-12

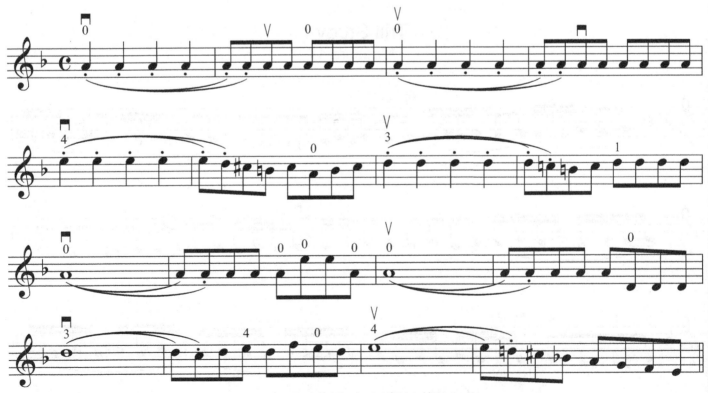

## Optional Hooked Bowing (Not Included in Main Exercises)
### Measure 18

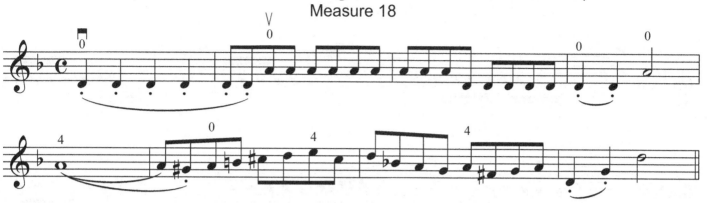

## Optional Hooked Bowing (Not Included in Main Exercises)
### Measures 41-43

## Optional Hooked Bowing (Not Included in Main Exercises): Measures 46-48

# Optional Hooked Bowing (Not Included in Main Exercises)
## Measures 55-57

# Optional Hooked Bowing (Not Included in Main Exercises)
## Measures 85-87

This page left blank
to help with page turns.

# Concerto: Violin One

J. S. Bach

This page left blank
to help with page turns.

# Concerto: Violin Two

J. S. Bach

# Concerto

J. S. Bach

J. S. Bach

2

# Classical Syncs; Duets for Two Violins, Book One

*from the 17th through the 20th Centuries*

## Allegro from *Concerto Grosso in d minor, RV 565*

A. Vivaldi, arr. M. Harvey

Made in the USA
Coppell, TX
23 January 2025